SCHOLASTIC

THE BOOK OF AWESOME KNOWLEDGE

7

Previously published as The Awesome GK Book by Scholastic India Pvt. Ltd.

Scholastic India Pvt. Ltd.
A-27, Ground Floor, Bharti Sigma Centre,
Infocity-1, Sector 34, Gurgaon (Haryana) 122001, India
Email: education@scholastic.co.in

Rest of the World
Scholastic Education International (Singapore) Pte Ltd
81 Ubi Avenue 4, #02-28 UB.ONE, Singapore 408830
Email: education@scholastic.com.sg

Visit our website: www.scholastic.co.in

First edition 2012
Reprinted 2012, 2014 (twice), 2015, 2016

ISBN: 978-81-8477-610-2

Printed at : Repro India Ltd., Mumbai

FSC
www.fsc.org
MIX
Paper from responsible sources
FSC® C047271

CONTENTS

 ISBN 978-81-8477-610-2

INTRODUCTION

Did you know that among Saturn's many, many moons are a very odd couple—Janus and Epimetheus? Every four years they swap orbits! Or did you know that a chameleon can move its eyes in two directions at the same time? Or that James Garfield, the twentieth president of the United States, could write Greek with one hand and Latin with the other—at the same time!

The Book of Awesome Knowledge is a collection of some really interesting, up-to-date information, some terribly crazy trivia and some downright disgusting facts mixed together with information a child is expected to know at each specific grade level. The subject-specific quizzes have been designed specifically to ensure that classroom lessons are reinforced in a fun and interesting way.

The topics covered in each book are linked to the curriculum prescribed by the national and state boards for that grade. The children are quizzed in a number of different interesting formats including crosswords, word hunts, true or false, matching pairs and multiple choice, among others. The nature and complexity of the quizzes are age- and grade-appropriate. Solving the quizzes requires minimal adult supervision—the language used is informal and child-friendly and the illustrations are wacky. We want the child to enjoy, relate to and absorb the information—not mug up boring data and answer a test paper.

 ISBN 978-81-8477-610-2

Each chapter is followed by a scorecard, which will help the children evaluate for themselves which subjects they are good at and where they need to pull up their socks.

The ultimate aim of this series is to make the child feel like a GK genius!

 ISBN 978-81-8477-610-2

AMAZING ANIMALS

How many of you have parents/grandparents who complain that you eat like a bird? Well, don't assume they think you are a fussy eater—they might be implying that you are a glutton because some birds are known to eat almost double their weight in a day!

 ISBN 978-81-8477-610-2

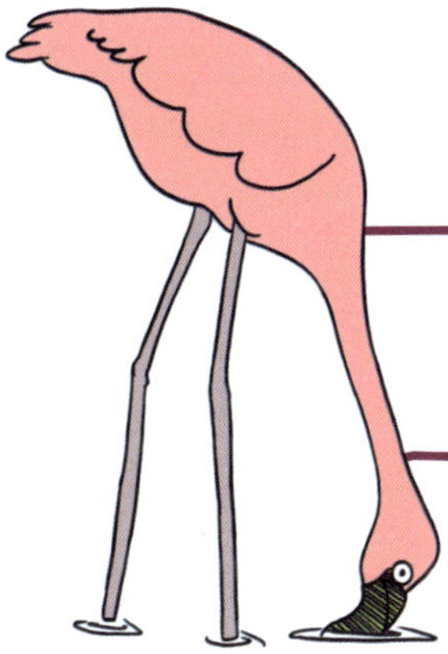

Talking of strange birds, did you know that a flamingo can eat only when its head is upside down!

Moving on to some more bizarre animals, here's information on some really rare and UGLY looking creatures. So the next time you want to come up with a really nasty nickname for the classmate/ neighbour who has been bugging you, you know where to pick the names. Incidentally, this is also a quiz. Some words are given in CAPITALS. Take the letters that appear in **BOLD** in them and unscramble them to solve the question given at the end of this section. Give yourself fifteen points if you crack the mystery word in less than seven minutes.

The depths of the ocean are literally swimming with creatures straight out of your weirdest nightmares and the V**IP**ER FI**SH** is among the scariest. This grotesque-looking creature has teeth so large they don't fit in its mouth. It swims at a very high speed towards its victims and impales them upon its sharp teeth!

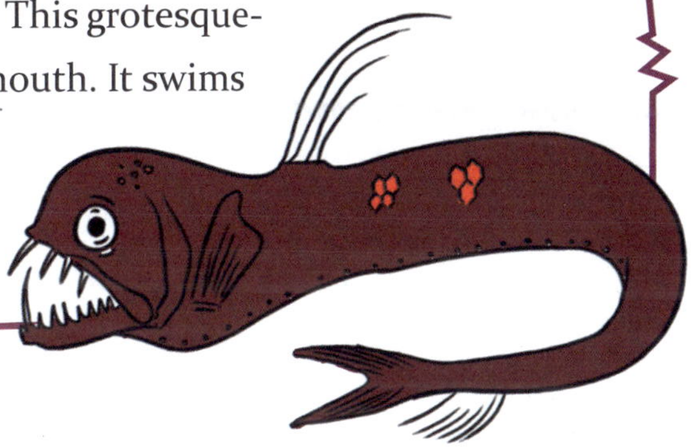

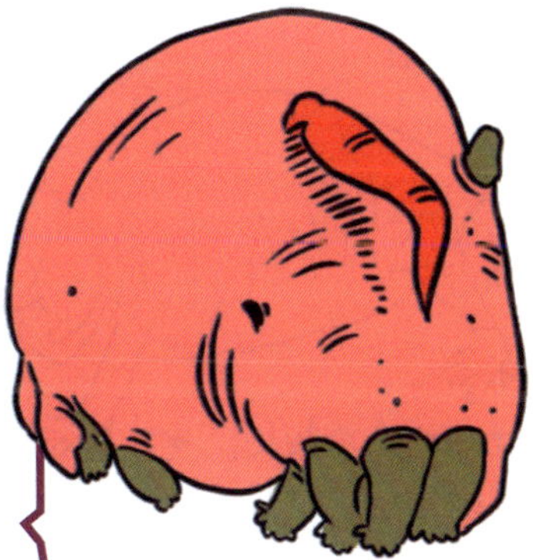

With its pale pink flesh, the SCO**T**OPLANE—known as the sea pig—resembles some kind of ugly growth. But, this strange creature is actually a type of sea cucumber. Sea pigs look and act sort of like slugs, feeding on organic materials that settle on the ocean floor.

 ISBN 978-81-8477-610-2

Few mammals are as weird looking as the endangered AYE-AYE, a lemur found only on the island of Madagascar. And guess what? It's actually a close relative of humans. With big protruding eyes, super-skinny fingers and a huge bushy tail, these creatures are pretty unique. Their bat-like ears allow them to detect insect larvae squirming inside trees.

Shaped somewhat like a tiny kangaroo, the nocturnal mouse-like LONG-EARED JERBOA uses its elongated tail and hind legs for jumping. The endangered rodent, found in the Gobi Desert of Mongolia, has ears that are about a third larger than its head and eats mostly insects.

Is it a porcupine or an anteater? Neither, actually. The LONG-BEAKED ECHIDNA is a rare egg-laying mammal found in Papua New Guinea. This nocturnal animal is a relative of the platypus. It lives underground where it uses its tube-like snout to search for invertebrate prey like insect larvae and worms. It has to eat soft food because it doesn't have any teeth.

Its wrinkled pink skin, piggish nose and protruding teeth don't exactly make the NAKED MOLE RAT the cutest animal around. Colonies of these hairless rodents live in underground "palaces" led by one dominant rat—the queen, which is the only female to breed and bear young. As with bees, naked mole rats have roles in the colony, including workers that dig the tunnels and gather food. Most naked mole rats are found in the sandy deserts of sub-Saharan Africa.

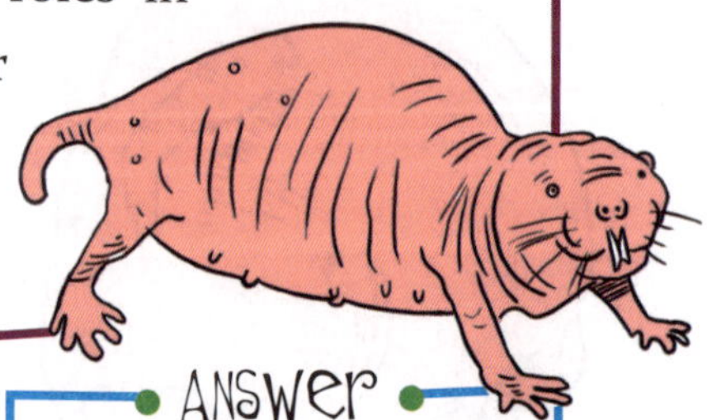

MY SCORE

The scientific term for flatworms is:

__ __ __ __ __ __ __ __ __ __ __ __ __ __ __ __

ANSWER

Platyhelmenthis

 ISBN 978-81-8477-610-2

That was really easy. Now, on to a multiple choice quiz. Give yourself a point for every correct answer.

1 Which of the following refers to a group of kittens?
a. An intrigue
b. A thriller
c. A suspense
d. A scheme

2 A baby eel is called
a. an ephyna.
b. a tadpole.
c. an elver.
d. a nymph.

3 A squab is a baby
a. dove.
b. clam.
c. squid.
d. otter.

4 What colour are flamingos when they are born?
a. Red
b. Pink
c. Grey
d. Black

5 Which of the following animals is not poisonous?
a. The pitohui bird
b. The diamondback rattlesnake
c. The fugu puffer fish
d. The poison arrow frog

6 The Dromedary and Bactrian are species of which animal?
a. Lizards
b. Snakes
c. Donkeys
d. Camels

 ISBN 978-81-8477-610-2

7 Why do many frogs and toads blow up their chin skin like a balloon?

a. Because they think it makes them look cool.
b. Because it helps cool them down.
c. Because it makes their calls louder.
d. To frighten adversaries.

8 What is a baby whale called?

a. Foal
b. Whalet
c. Fry
d. Calf

9 Which animal is also known as the water horse?

a. Rhino
b. Hippo
c. Okapi
d. Zebra

10 This long haired animal is a Tibetan member of the cow family.

a. Yak
b. Buffalo
c. Dhole
d. Saiga

Answers

1. a. An intrigue. Other collective names for a group of kittens are "kindle" and "litter". | 2. c. It's hard to think of some of these animals as babies. A nymph is a baby cockroach (the young of some other insects are also called nymphs) and an ephyna is a baby jellyfish. | 3. a. It originally meant "a very young bird". | 4. c. Flamingos turn pink from eating large amounts of shrimp and plankton which is what their diet largely consists of. | 5. b. The pitohui is a strange little New Guinea bird whose feathers are coated with poison. The fugu is a Japanese delicacy that can kill if improperly prepared. Poison arrow frogs secrete toxins through glands in their skin. Rattlesnakes are not toxic if ingested—like most strange animals, they are said to taste like chicken! 6. d. | 7. c. Male frogs and toads make loud calls to attract females. | 8. d. | 9. b. | 10. a.

MY SCORE

 ISBN 978-81-8477-610-2

BET YOU DIDN'T KNOW...

Bet you didn't know that a rat can last longer without water than a camel can.

 ISBN 978-81-8477-610-2

Here's a quick [T] = TRUE or [F] = FALSE quiz. Give yourself one point for each correct answer and a bonus point if you finish them all in less than two minutes.

1. The ostrich is the fastest bird in the world. [T] [F]
2. The koala belongs to the bear family. [T] [F]
3. A turtle is a reptile. [T] [F]
4. Horses can swim. [T] [F]
5. Camels store water in their humps. [T] [F]
6. Sharks are mammals. [T] [F]
7. Crocodiles have claws. [T] [F]
8. Ducks have see-through eyelids. [T] [F]
9. A young zebra's stripes start out as brown and darken as it grows. [T] [F]
10. Snakes can't blink. [T] [F]

MY SCORE [ ] + BONUS POINT [ ] = [ ]

Answers

1. True | 2. False | 3. True | 4. True | 5. False | 6. False | 7. True | 8. True | 9. True | 10. True

Final Score

- [ ] 36–30 Avid animal enthusiast!
- [ ] 29–20 Keep up the good work!
- [ ] 19 AND BELOW All animals don't bite! Get to know them a bit better.

 ISBN 978-81-8477-610-2

PECULIAR PLANTS

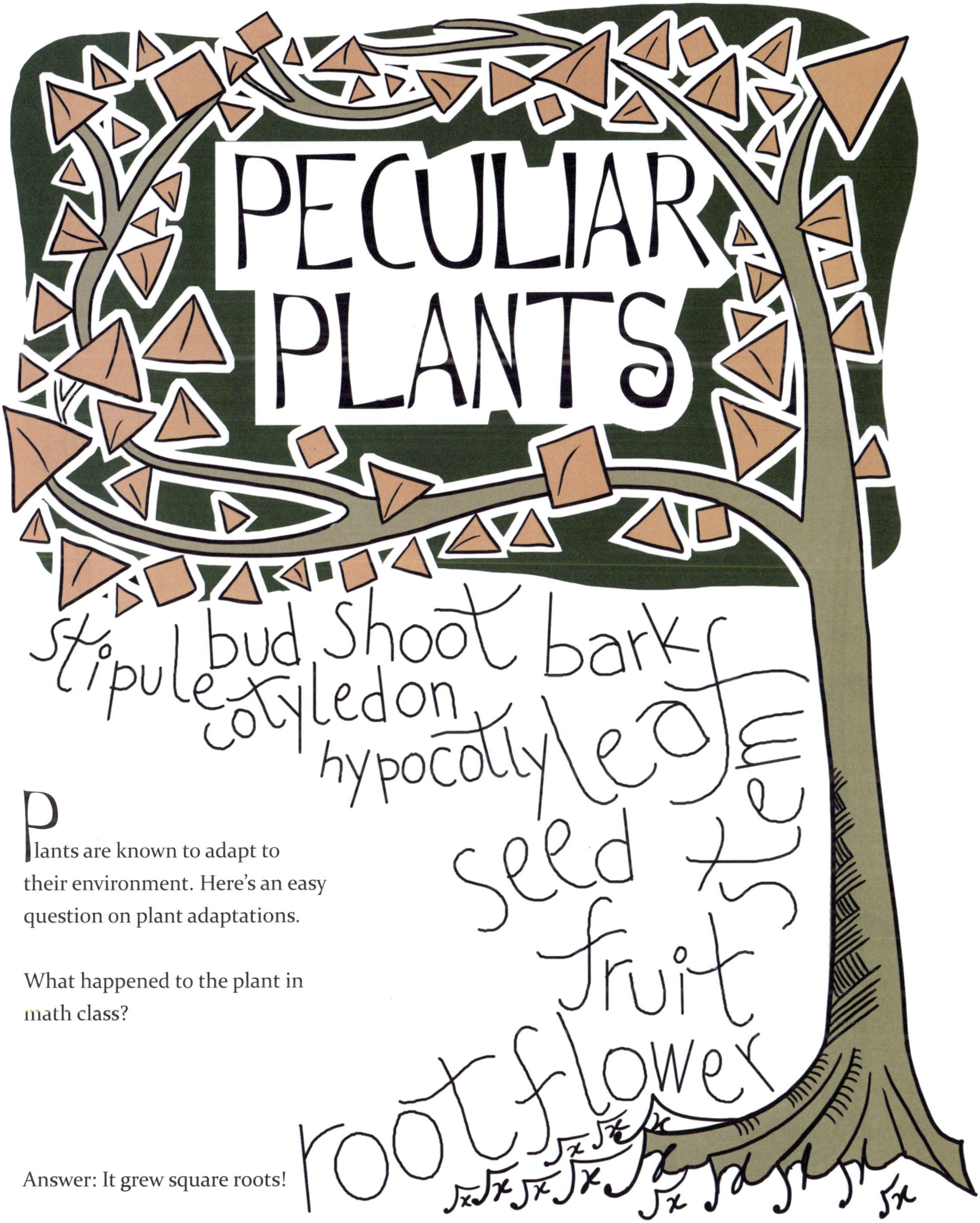

Plants are known to adapt to their environment. Here's an easy question on plant adaptations.

What happened to the plant in math class?

Answer: It grew square roots!

 ISBN 978-81-8477-610-2

Okay, that was a trick question! On to proper plant questions. Given below is a multiple choice quiz. Pick the correct option. Give yourself a point for each correct answer.

1. Plants react to stimuli at a __________ rate than animals.
   a. faster
   b. slower
   c. similar

2. Germinating seeds respire at a __________ rate compared to leaves.
   a. faster
   b. slower
   c. similar rate

3. The organic matter in soil is known as __________.
   a. silt
   b. alluvium
   c. humus

4. Seeds with two cotyledons are called __________.
   a. dicots
   b. polycots
   c. spores

5. Wheat, barley and corn can be classified as __________.
   a. fruits
   b. cereals
   c. vegetables

 ISBN 978-81-8477-610-2

6 Sugar cane, bamboo and wheat belong to the same family.

a. True

b. False

7 The ______ of turnips, carrots and radish are edible.

a. roots

b. stems

c. flowers

8 Which of the following is not of plant origin?

a. pearl

b. paper

c. rubber

9 Which plant does not have chlorophyll?

a. poppy

b. fern

c. mushroom

10 The seeds of coniferous trees are contained in ________.

a. flowers

b. fruits

c. cones

MY SCORE

Answers

1. b | 2. a | 3. c | 4. a | 5. b | 6. a | 7. a | 8. a | 9. c | 10. c

 ISBN 978-81-8477-610-2

Bet you didn't know...

Bet you didn't know that the world's oldest living plant is a Bristlecone pine nicknamed Methuselah. It is located in the White Mountains of California. This Bristlecone pine is an amazing 4,841 years old!

Here's a plant crossword. Give yourself a point for each word that you solve.

ACROSS

3. Specialised stem that coils around or sticks to objects (found in grapevines)
4. The stalk that joins a leaf to a stem
5. Vascular tissue that conducts water in a plant
7. Flowering plants are classified as
8. The whorls of petals of a flower
9. A plant that lives for more than two years

DOWN

1. Gases enter and leave the leaf through these openings
2. Plants with one cotyledon
4. Vascular tissue that conducts food in a plant
6. Underground stem that grows horizontally (for example, ginger)

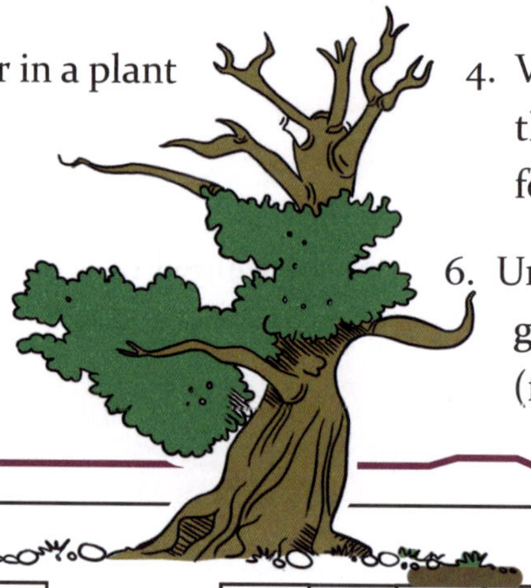

 ISBN 978-81-8477-610-2

Answers

ACROSS - 3. tendril | 4. petiole | 5. xylem | 7. angiosperms | 8. corolla | 9. perennial
DOWN - 1. stomata | 2. monocots | 4. phloem | 6. rhizome

MY SCORE

Why do potatoes make excellent detectives?

Answer: Because they keep their eyes peeled!

On a more serious note, here's the final section of the Peculiar Plant quiz. In this section you simply need to answer the following questions. Give yourself a point for each correct answer.

1. Apart from sugar cane, which other plant is grown commercially as a source of sugar? ____________________
2. *Amrapali, Dussehri, Chausa* and *Totapuri* are varieties of which very well-loved fruit? ____________________
3. The diet of the giant panda comprises almost exclusively of which plant? ____________________
4. What substance are the cell walls of plants made? ____________________
5. What are mosses and worts known as? ____________________
6. What is the technical name of a swollen, underground storage stem adapted for storage and reproduction *(hint: potato)*? ____________________

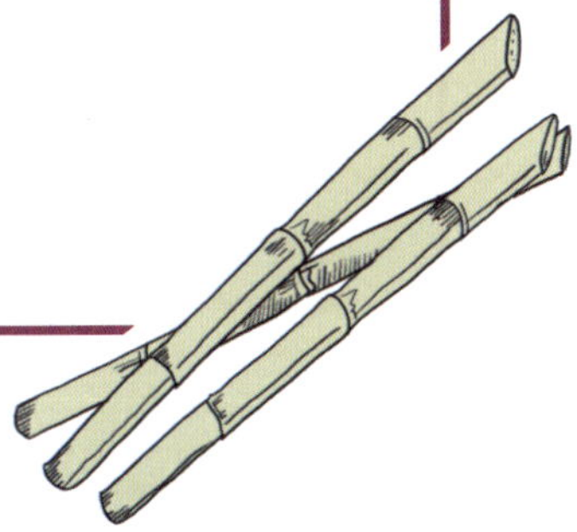

 ISBN 978-81-8477-610-2

7. What is the term used for the part of the stem from which a leaf, branch or aerial root grows? ____________________

8. What part of the plant is referred to as the lamina? ____________________

9. Chrysanthemum is the crest of which imperial family? ____________________

10. What is the arrangement of veins on a leaf blade called? ____________________

Answers

1. Sugar beet | 2. Mango. BTW, did you know that mangoes belong to the same botanical family as cashew nuts, peppers and pistachios! | 3. Bamboo | 4. Cellulose | 5. Bryophytes | 6. Tuber 7. Node | 8. The leaf blade | 9. The Japanese royal family | 10. Venation

MY SCORE

Final Scores

☐ 30–25 Excellent!

☐ 24–15 Good!

☐ 14 AND BELOW Try harder next time!

 ISBN 978-81-8477-610-2

STRANGE SCIENCE

galaxy planet asteroid comet constellation sun star gases meteoroid satellite

ISBN 978-81-8477-610-2

Here's a quiz to try if you are feeling a little "spaced out". Try to whiz through this quiz at a super stellar speed. Give yourself a point for each correct answer and a bonus point if you manage to get all answers correct.

1. Which planet in our solar system takes about 11.9 years to orbit the sun? ________________

2. Which planet in our solar system has the most circular orbit? ________________

3. What's the term for the point in the orbit of a planet or comet where it is farthest from the earth? ________________

4. How long does it take the sun to rotate about its axis once? ________________

5. Which planet in our solar system takes less than ten hours to rotate around its axis? ________________

6. Which planet does the satellite Pandora orbit? ________________

7. What are the names of the two satellites that orbit Mars? ________________

8. Which astronomer first proposed the theory that the earth revolves around the sun? ________________

9. On which planet can you find the Great Red Spot? ________________

MY SCORE [ ] + BONUS POINT [ ] = [ ]

Answers

1. Jupiter | 2. Venus | 3. Apogee | 4. Twenty-eight earth days | 5. Jupiter | 6. Saturn | 7. Deimos and Phobos (They are really tiny satellites—both are only a few kilometers across. They are probably asteroids that were pulled in by the gravity of Mars.) | 8. Nicolaus Copernicus | 9. Jupiter (The Great Red Spot is actually a storm that has been blowing for the last 300 years!)

 ISBN 978-81-8477-610-2

• BET YOU DIDN'T KNOW... •

Bet you didn't know that among Saturn's many, many moons are a very odd couple—Janus and Epimetheus. Every four years they swap orbits!

Just to keep you from getting bored, here are two Quick Five quizzes. In the first quiz, you need to match the fabulous invention to its even more fabulous inventor. Give yourself a point for each correct answer. You have a time limit of forty-five seconds.

1	John Hopps	a.	air conditioner
2	Rudolf Diesel	b.	dynamo/electric generator
3	Werner von Siemens	c.	blood banks
4	Willis Haviland Carrier	d.	combustion engine
5	Charles Drew	e.	cardiac pacemaker

Answers

1. e. Canadian John Hopps invented the first cardiac pacemaker. Hopps was trained as an electrical engineer. While experimenting with radio frequency heating to restore body temperature, Hopps made an unexpected discovery: if a heart stopped beating due to cooling, it could be started again by artificial stimulation using mechanical or electric means. This lead to Hopps' invention of the world's first cardiac pacemaker in 1950.

2. d. | 3. b. | 4. a. This cool inventor patented his idea for the air-conditioner as an "apparatus for treating air".

5. c. Drew was an African-American physician and medical researcher. He researched in the field of blood transfusions, developing improved techniques for blood storage and applied his expert knowledge in developing large-scale blood banks early during World War II, saving thousands of lives of the Allied forces.

MY SCORE

 ISBN 978-81-8477-610-2

In this next Quick Five quiz, you need to match the standard units of measurement with what they are used to measure. Give yourself a point for each correct answer. But you have a time limit of thirty seconds!

1	Watts	a.	radio frequency
2	Fahrenheit	b.	distance in space
3	Light years	c.	luminous intensity
4	Candela	d.	electrical power
5	Hertz	e.	temperature

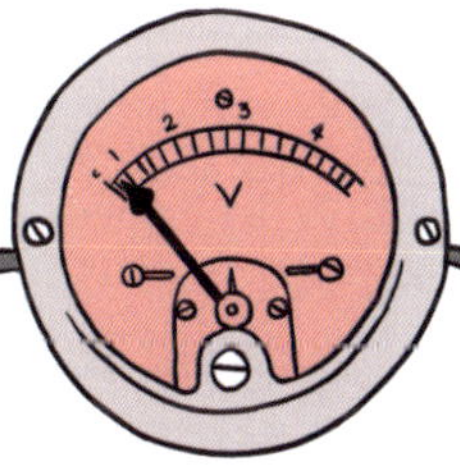

Answers

1. d | 2. e | 3. b | 4. c | 5. a

MY SCORE

 ISBN 978-81-8477-610-2

Have a look at the strange science statements given here. You are allowed only two options—declare in a very serious and sage voice "How true" or make your most dismissive face and say "What a load of rubbish!" In other words, you've got to indicate whether the following statements are T = TRUE or F = FALSE. Give yourself a point for each correct answer.

1. Water can be used to cut metal, rock, leather and paper. T F

2. Good weather makes you thinner. T F

3. The gravity of planet Jupiter sucks in comets and stops them from hitting earth. T F

4. Gold is so easy to roll flat that you could melt a lump the size of a matchbox and use it to cover a tennis court. T F

5. Rabbits are coprophagous animals. *(FYI, coprophagous animals are those that eat their own poo!)* T F

6. Forest fires move faster uphill than downhill. T F

7. You would feel less air pressure at the beach than you would in the mountains. T F

 ISBN 978-81-8477-610-2

8 Sharks have very strong and flexible bones. T F

9 Matter that does not enter into a chemical reaction is said to be radioactive. T F

10 The smallest unit of a substance that retains the properties of the substance is the molecule. T F

Answers

1. True. In industries, water-cutting uses fine high-pressure sprays mixed with tiny bits of grit. It is used to cut through metals, stones, plastics, etc. | 2. True. In bright, sunny weather, the air pressure is greater and this squeezes your bulging body and makes you feel leaner and fitter. In cold, miserable weather, the opposite occurs and you feel fat and bloated. 3. True. If it wasn't for Jupiter's amazing comet-trapping abilities, earth would have been wiped out a long time ago. 4. True | 5. Disgusting, but true. Rabbits eat their own dung. Plants such as grass are quite hard to digest and rabbits get around this problem by digesting their food twice—once as food and once as poo. 6. True | 7. False. Air pressure decreases with altitude. | 8. False. Unlike most other fish, a shark has no bones! Its skeleton is made of cartilage, a material somewhat softer and more flexible than bone. 9. False. Matter that does not enter into a chemical reaction is said to be inert. | 10. True

MY SCORE

Final Scores

- ☐ 30–25 Stellar performance!
- ☐ 24–20 Astronomical!
- ☐ 19–15 A bit spaced out?
- ☐ 14 AND BELOW Eclipsed!

 ISBN 978-81-8477-610-2

HEALTHY HUMAN BODY

Don't ever stick out your tongue at the teacher or the police if you want to hide your identity, that is. Similar to fingerprints, everyone also has a unique tongue print!

BET YOU DIDN'T KNOW...

Bet you didn't know *(and this is bound to make your skin crawl)* that every square inch of skin on the human body has about thirty-two million bacteria on it, but fortunately, the vast majority of them are harmless!

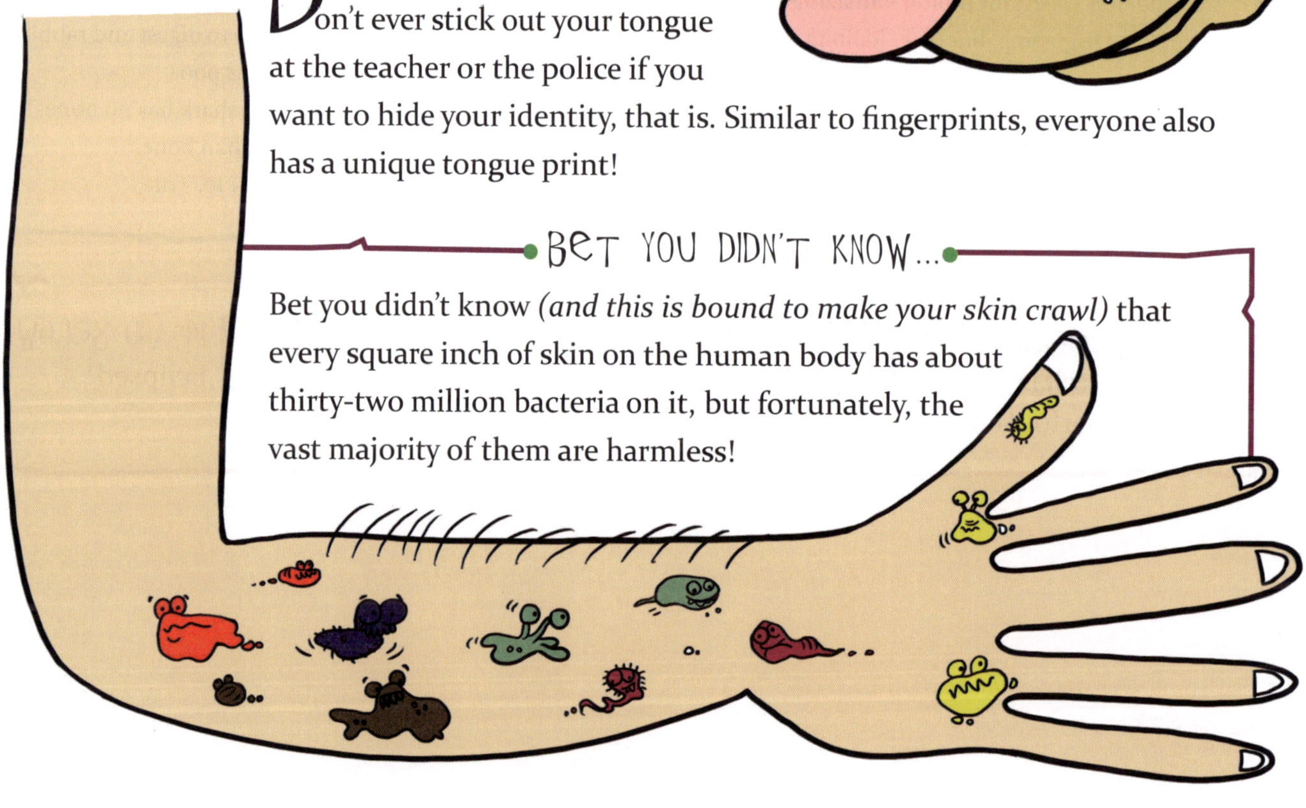

 ISBN 978-81-8477-610-2

Here are a few questions to see how well you *think* you know your body.

In this quiz, each question has only two possible answers—so even if you just guess, you'll still have a 50 per cent chance of being right!

1. Who has the higher body temperature? Boys or girls?
2. Deficiency of which vitamin leads to problems with how fast your blood clots? Vitamin E or Vitamin K?
3. How fast can nerve impulses move to and from the brain? A mind-boggling 270 km per hour or a steady 50 km per hour?
4. What is the title given to a doctor who specialises in treating infants and kids? Dermatologist or paediatrician?
5. Who has more bones? A full grown adult or a child?

6. Which is the largest gland in your body? The thyroid gland or the liver?
7. What causes hay fever? Hay or pollen?
8. What purpose do wisdom teeth serve? Do they make you wiser or do they serve no purpose at all?
9. Where does sea-sickness (or motion sickness) start? In your stomach or in your ear?
10. Do your brain cells die? Yes or no?

 ISBN 978-81-8477-610-2

Answers

1. Girls by 0.3 °C. BTW boys, that doesn't make you "cooler" than girls! 2. Vitamin K, which you find in leafy veggies, meat and liver, is essential for blood coagulation. | 3. Believe it or not, nerve impulses can move up to speeds of 270 km per hour! 4. A paediatrician. A dermatologist is a doctor who specialises in treating abnormalities and diseases of the skin. | 5. A child! You probably figured that because an adult is bigger, he would have more bones in his body. But that isn't so! An infant has 300 bones in its body, while an adult has only 206. What happens to them as the child grows? Do they just disappear? No! As the child grows, two or three of these bones fuse, or grow together, to form one bone. | 6. The liver. Most people know that the liver is the largest organ in the body but many don't realise that it's also a gland. A gland is defined as any organ or part of an organ that secretes substances. The liver, in addition to its many functions like detoxifying blood, storing sugars, etc., also secretes bile (a fluid that both aids in digestion and transports fats as well as waste products to the intestine.). | 7. Pollen. Many people are allergic to the pollen of certain plants, and the sickness they suffer from this pollen is called hay fever. Though hay fever is not often caused by pollen from hay, the allergy is called hay fever because it was first described by an English doctor who noticed that it always appeared during the haying season. | 8. They serve no purpose at all. Normally, you will have developed a full set of teeth (including two sets of molars) by the age of 13. Some people develop a third set of molars around the age of 18. These molars are called wisdom teeth because they appear later in a person's life, when he/she is "supposedly" wiser. They usually cause so much pain as they come in that they have to be pulled out. The reason for that pain is because the human skull is shaped differently today than it was many thousands of years ago. So, wisdom teeth don't serve any real purpose apart from making a few dentists rich! | 9. Ears. Sea-sickness may feel like it begins in the stomach but it actually starts in the ears! Your sense of balance is controlled by canals filled with lymph inside the ears. Now, when you're on a ship that is rocking back and forth or if you are winding up a steep mountain road in a fast car, the lymph rocks back and forth too, sending messages to the brain that keep changing as your position changes. Eventually, these changing messages "overload" the brain and confuse the nervous system. This confusion produces the nausea, dizziness, sweating and other discomforts we call sea-sickness or motion sickness. | 10. Yes. At a certain age, your brain stops growing. You stay alive, but some of your brain cells die and are not replaced. In fact, after the age of 18, a person may lose more than a thousand brain cells each day! But there's no danger of your brain ever "burning out" because there are over 100 billion nerve cells in your brain. At the rate of a thousand brain cells lost per day, it would take almost 300,000 years before your brain ran out of cells!

MY SCORE

 ISBN 978-81-8477-610-2

Learnt some new stuff about your body? Great! Here's a simple quiz in which you need to match the specialists with their fields of specialisation. Give yourself a point for each correct answer. So, what are you waiting for? On your marks, get set, GO!

1. cardiologist
2. gynaecologist
3. haematologist
4. ophthalmologist
5. nephrologist
6. urologist
7. orthopaedist
8. hepatologist
9. endocrinologist
10. neurologist

a. nervous system
b. liver
c. bones
d. urinary tract
e. heart
f. female reproductive system
g. blood
h. eyes
i. kidneys
j. endocrine gland

MY SCORE

ANSWERS

1. e | 2. f | 3. g | 4. h | 5. i | 6. d | 7. c | 8. b | 9. j | 10. a

BET YOU DIDN'T KNOW...

Bet you didn't know that you get a new stomach lining every three to four days! If you didn't, the strong acids your stomach uses to digest food would also digest your stomach!

ISBN 978-81-8477-610-2

Here is the final section of the Human Body quiz. You have to provide a simple one-word answer for the following questions. Give yourself a point for each correct answer.

1. What is the full form of AIDS? ______________________

2. Which is the only organ in the human body that, if partially removed, grows back to its original size? ______________________

3. What is the name of the disease caused by an abnormal increase in white blood cells? ______________________

4. Which grow faster—fingernails or toenails? ______________________

5. Which mineral (often found in toothpastes) helps prevent tooth decay? ______________

6. What is the hardest substance in the human body? ______________

 ISBN 978-81-8477-610-2

7 How many muscles are there in the human body? ______________________

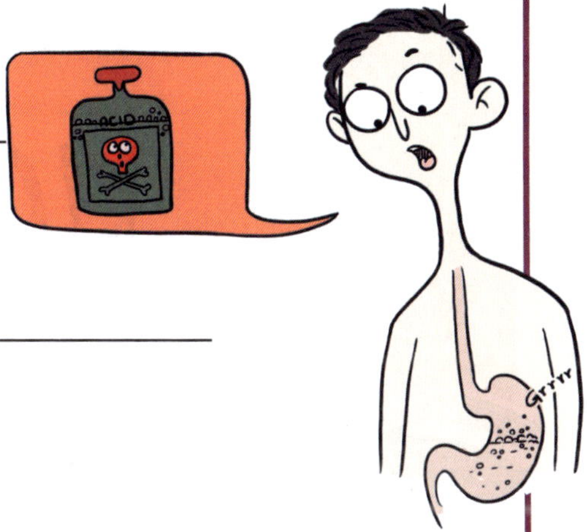

8 What is the name of the acid found in the human stomach? ______________________

9 Which is the largest artery in the body? ______________________

10 How many chambers are there in the human heart? ______________________

MY SCORE

ANSWERS

1. acquired immune deficiency syndrome | 2. liver | 3. leukaemia | 4. fingernails | 5. fluoride
6. enamel | 7. 650 | 8. hydrochloric acid | 9. aorta | 10. four

FINAL SCORE

- ☐ 30–25 Hale and hearty score!
- ☐ 24–15 Healthy score!
- ☐ 14 AND BELOW Sickly!

 ISBN 978-81-8477-610-2

 ISBN 978-81-8477-610-2

Here's the family tree of the Great Mughals. A brief description of each emperor is provided and a few letters of each royalty's name are provided. See if you can figure out the names in less than two minutes. Give yourself a point for each name you can identify correctly. Give yourself four bonus points if you solve this quiz within four minutes.

1 He was the founder of the Mughal dynasty. He started out as a ruler of Kabul. He invaded India and defeated Ibrahim Lodi at the First Battle of Panipat in 1526. Instead of looting all the goodies and returning home, he decided to stay back in India.

B _ _ _ _

2 He had to fight many wars against the wily Afghan chief Sher Shah Suri, who eventually chased him out of his Indian territories. But being a tenacious warrior, he returned from Persia fifteen years later and regained his territories. He expanded the Mughal Empire and left his son a huge empire to reign over.

_ U _ _ Y _ _

3 He ascended the throne at the age of thirteen. During his reign, he eliminated military threats from the Pashtun descendants of Sher Shah Suri and at the Second Battle of Panipat he defeated the Hindu king Hemu. He brought most of north and central India into his realm. He brought about many reforms that helped strengthen his empire. He also founded a new religion—Din-i-Illahi, which unfortunately didn't catch on like he hoped it would.

_ K _ _ _

 ISBN 978-81-8477-610-2

4 Also known as Prince Salim, he rebelled against his father and tried to take over the throne by force. Although this attempt to usurp the throne was in vain, he did ultimately succeed his father as the emperor. Like his father before him, he too was interested in ensuring justice in his empire.

J _ _ _ _ _ _ _

5 He was known as Prince Khurram before he ascended the throne.
He is perhaps best remembered for the Taj Mahal, the famous mausoleum built in honour of his wife, Mumtaz Mahal.

_ H _ _ J _ _ _ _

6 After the death of his father, he defeated his brothers and became the emperor.
Though he ruled the Mughal Empire for almost fifty years, it had weakened considerably by the time he died. His successors were not strong and were not able to hold the empire together.

_ U _ _ _ G _ _ _

MY SCORE + BONUS POINTS =

Answers

1. Babur | 2. Humayun | 3. Akbar | 4. Jehangir
5. Shah Jahan | 6. Aurangzeb

 ISBN 978-81-8477-610-2

If you haven't been doodling, day-dreaming or plain snoozing in your history class, the next set of questions should be a breeze for you. Plus, it's a multiple choice quiz, which means the answers are already there and you just have to make the right choice. Give yourself a point for each correct answer. See how many you can answer in five minutes.

1. The Grand Trunk Road was built by ____________.
   a. Babur
   b. Sher Shah Suri
   c. Inspector Gadget
   d. Lord Mountbatten

2. Megasthenes, the Greek ambassador, visited the court of __________.
   a. Ashoka
   b. Kanishka
   c. Alexander the Great
   d. Chandragupta Maurya

3. Fatehpur Sikri was built by ____________.
   a. Jehangir
   b. Shah Jahan
   c. Akbar
   d. Aurangzeb

4. The famous Brihadisvara Temple in Thanjavur was built in the reign of ________.
   a. King Rajaraja Chola
   b. King Vijayalaya Chola
   c. King Rajadhiraj Chola II
   d. King Rajendra Chola I

5. The first Viceroy of India was ____________.
   a. Lord Dalhousie
   b. Lord Canning
   c. Lord Elgin
   d. Lord Mayo

 ISBN 978-81-8477-610-2

6. ____________ was a Chinese Buddhist monk who made a seventeen-year trip to India in the seventh century and studied Buddhist scriptures at Nalanda.
a. Zhang Qian
b. Fa Hien
c. Hiuen Tsang
d. Jackie Chan

7. The __________ is the most frequently occurring symbol on the Sanchi Stupa.
a. deer
b. peacock
c. Buddha
d. lotus

8. The Mesopotamian Civilisation flourished around the ___________river system.
a. Indus
b. Tigris–Euphrates
c. Nile
d. Amazon

9. The famous king __________ was NOT part of the Gupta Dynasty.
a. Chandragupta Maurya
b. Chandra Gupta I
c. Samudragupta
d. Vikramaditya

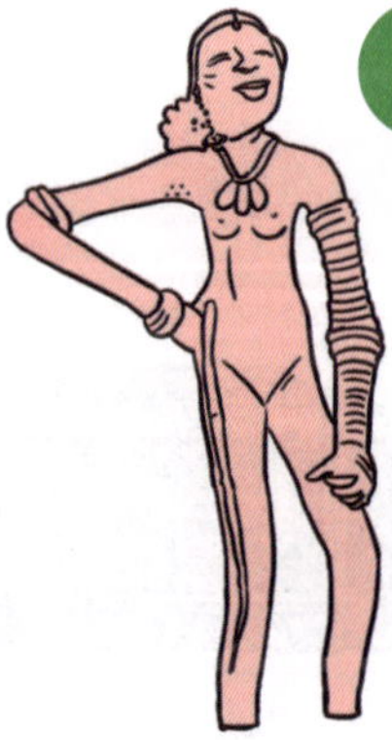

10. The figurine of the dancing girl and the bust of the "priest king", both very famous artifacts of the Indus Valley Civilisation, were excavated at _________.
a. Lothal
b. Mohenjo-daro
c. Harappa
d. Mehrgarh

MY SCORE

ANSWERS

1. b | 2. d | 3. c | 4. a | 5. b | 6. c | 7. d | 8. b | 9. a | 10. b

 ISBN 978-81-8477-610-2

That must have been a very easy quiz for you. Now, on to something that will make you think about how well you know your timelines. Arrange the following major world events in chronological order from the earliest (1) to the most recent (5). Give yourself a point for each correct answer.

- ◯ French Revolution ____________
- ◯ Bombing of Nagasaki and Hiroshima ____________
- ◯ World War I ____________
- ◯ Formation of the United Nations ____________
- ◯ The Sepoy Mutiny ____________

Answers

1. French Revolution (1789–1799) | 2. Sepoy Mutiny (1857) | 3. World War I (1914–1918)
4. Bombing of Hiroshima and Nagasaki (6 and 9 August 1945 [respectively])
5. Formation of the United Nations (24 October 1945)

MY SCORE

 ISBN 978-81-8477-610-2

The final quiz in the Horrible History section is on famous structures from around the world. You need to indicate in which part of the world they can be found *(mention the city where each structure is located, or simply the name of the country where they are to be found)*. Give yourself a point for each correct answer.

1. Champs Élysées ____________________
2. Shore Temple ____________________
3. Sun Temple ____________________
4. Statue of Liberty ____________________
5. Machu Picchu ____________________
6. Christ the Redeemer ____________________
7. Humayun's Tomb ____________________
8. Colosseum ____________________
9. Char Minar ____________________
10. The Great Pyramids ____________________

MY SCORE

Answers

1. Paris, France | 2. Mahabalipuram, India | 3. Konark, India | 4. New York, USA | 5. Peru
6. Rio de Janeiro, Brazil | 7. New Delhi, India | 8. Rome, Italy | 9. Hyderabad, India | 10. Giza, Egypt

Final Score

☐ 35–25 Horribly good at history!

☐ 24–20 Not bad!

☐ 19–15 Ho-hum in history!

☐ 14 and below Try harder next time!

 ISBN 978-81-8477-610-2

GARGANTUAN GEOGRAPHY

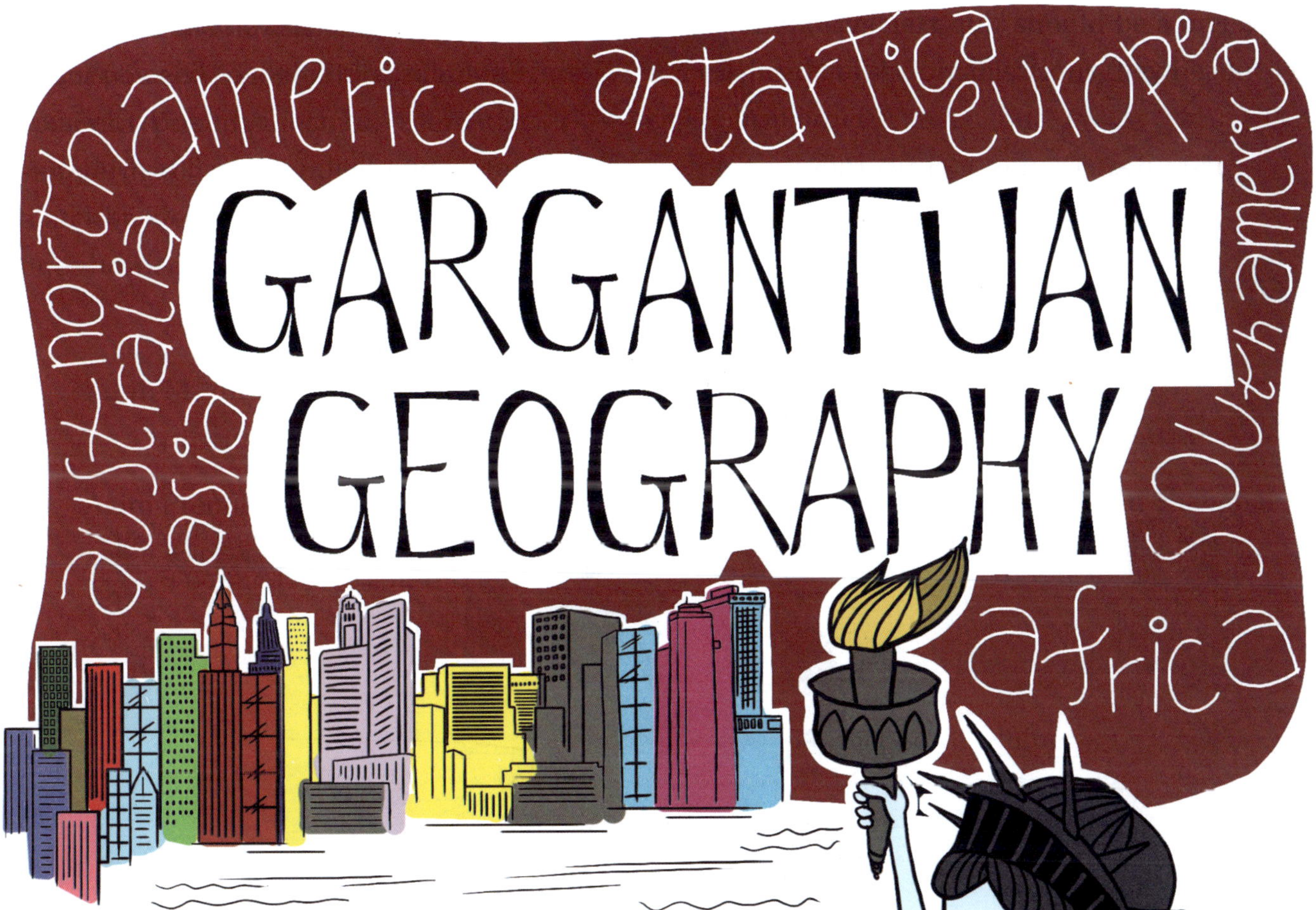

Here are some serious geography questions for you—think hard before you answer.

1. Why does the Statue of Liberty stand in New York Habour?
Answer: Because it can't sit down.

2. What do Amitabh Bachchan and a map scale have in common?
Answer: They are both legends!

3. Why was longitude boiling mad?
Answer: Because it was 360°!

 ISBN 978-81-8477-610-2

Okay, those were *really* pathetic geography jokes. Promise no more PJs—only serious stuff from here on. Given below are five questions each on four geographical features. Give yourself a point for each correct answer and a bonus point if you get all correct.

First up are islands. Identify these very famous islands based on the information provided.

1. It is the world's largest island and is part of the kingdom of Denmark.

2. Situated in the Indian and Pacific oceans, the Great Barrier Reef is one of the main landmarks of this island nation.

3. This island is the largest producer of sugar in the world. It is known by its sobriquet "Pearl of the Antilles".

4. This island nation lies to the east of Norway. Its capital is Reykjavik.

5. This island nation is situated in the Indian Ocean. It comprises a double chain of twenty-six atolls. In late 2009, the government of this island nation held a cabinet meeting underwater to highlight the threat of global warming to the low-lying Indian Ocean nation.

MY SCORE + BONUS POINT =

Answers

1. Greenland | 2. Australia | 3. Cuba | 4. Iceland | 5. Maldives

 ISBN 978-81-8477-610-2

Wasn't that easy? Here's the next section on water bodies or to be very specific, straits. *(You know what they are, don't you? A strait is a narrow, navigable channel of water that connects two larger navigable bodies of water.)*

Take a guess at where these famous straits are located. Give yourself a point for each correct answer.

1. Bass Strait ______________________
2. Bering Strait ______________________
3. Dire Straits ______________________
4. Cook Strait ______________________
5. Strait of Dover ______________________
6. Palk Strait ______________________

Answers

1. It is located between mainland Australia and Tasmania and connects the Southern Ocean with the Pacific Ocean.
2. It is located between Alaska and Siberia. It connects the Pacific and Arctic oceans.
3. Hee, hee, hee. Gotcha! That was a trick question! Dire Straits is not a geographical feature—they are a very famous rock group of the Ancient Age (think 1970s, 1980s!). Maybe your folks have a copy of their famous songs like *Sultans of Swing* or *Money for Nothing*.
4. It separates the North and South Islands of New Zealand. It's named after Captain James Cook, a British sailor, who was the first to circumnavigate New Zealand.
5. It lies between England and France and connects the North Sea with the English Channel.
6. It lies between Tamil Nadu and Sri Lanka. This area is very rich in natural resources.

MY SCORE

 ISBN 978-81-8477-610-2

Next up are rivers. Identify these phenomenal rivers. Give yourself a point for each correct answer and a bonus point if you get all correct.

1. Longest river in the world. ____________________

2. The river with the most number of tributaries. ____________________

3. The longest river in China and Asia. ____________________

4. The longest river in Europe. ____________________

5. The longest river in North America. ____________________

MY SCORE + BONUS POINT =

Answers

1. Nile | 2. Amazon. Did you know that the Amazon has 200 tributaries! It carries more water than any other river in the world. In fact, the Amazon River is responsible for about one-fifth (20 per cent) of the fresh water that flows into the world's oceans. | 3. Yangtze | 4. Volga. It flows primarily in a southerly direction through Russia into the Caspian Sea.
5. Mississippi River. The Missouri is one of the main tributaries of this river.

 ISBN 978-81-8477-610-2

The last section of the quiz is on a very *dry* topic—deserts. Identify these famous deserts. Give yourself a point for each correct answer and a bonus point if you get all correct.

1. A cold desert in Asia. ____________________

2. The largest desert in the world. ____________________

3. The only desert in India. ____________________

4. The coldest desert in the world.
(*Hint: It's also a continent!*) ____________________

5. Driest desert in the world.
(*Hint: It's in South America.*) ____________________

MY SCORE [ ] + BONUS POINT [ ] = [ ]

Answers

1. Gobi Desert | 2. Sahara Desert | 3. Thar Desert | 4. Antarctica | 5. Atacama Desert

 ISBN 978-81-8477-610-2

For this next quiz, you need to imagine that you have the magical ability to travel to any world capital in the blink of an eye. You blink your eye and *poof*! You are in an exotic country, speaking the local language, munching on its famous delicacies and your pocket is stuffed with the local currency.

All you need to do in this quiz is to identify the country you are most likely to be in from all the information given to you. Give yourself a point for each correct answer and a bonus point if you get all correct.

CITY YOU HAVE LANDED IN	YOU ARE MUNCHING ON	THE LANGUAGE THE NATIVES ARE SPEAKING IN
Düsseldorf	Sausages, pretzels, black forest cake 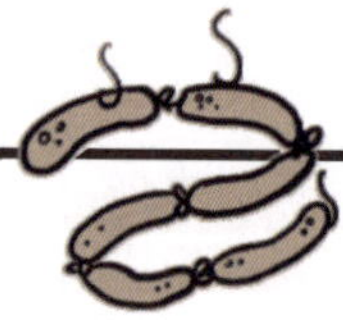	German
Barcelona 	Paella, gazpacho	Spanish
Yokohama	Sushi, sashimi 	Japanese
Shanghai 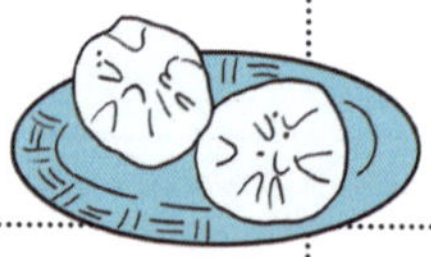	Nian gao (yummy sticky cakes), char siu bao (steamed buns with barbequed meat filling)	Cantonese
Chittagong	Biryani, jhal muri, shondesh 	Bangla

 ISBN 978-81-8477-610-2

THE CURRENCY IN YOUR POCKET	WHAT COMES OUT OF YOUR MOUTH WHEN YOU WANT TO SAY "HI"	THE COUNTRY YOU ARE MOST LIKELY IN
Euro	Guten Tag!	________________
Euro	Hola!	________________
Yen	Ohaiyo Gonzaimasu! (that is, if you are saying Good Morning!)	________________
Yuan	Nee how!	________________
Taka	Asalaam alaykum!	________________

MY SCORE [ ] + BONUS POINT [ ] = [ ]

ANSWERS

1. Germany | 2. Spain | 3. Japan | 4. China | 5. Bangladesh

FINAL SCORE

☐ 30–25 Geography genius!

☐ 24–15 Good!

☐ 14 AND BELOW Time to flip through a geography book.

 ISBN 978-81-8477-610-2

SUPER SPORTS

BET YOU DIDN'T KNOW...

Bet you didn't know that soccer is the world's most popular sport. It is played by more than 20 million people in more than 140 countries.

 ISBN 978-81-8477-610-2

The next quiz is for the *ultimate football-crazy person*. But if you are not *the ultimate football crazy fan*, use your common sense (and language skills) for this quiz. You need to identify which country the following football clubs belong to. Give yourself a point for each correct answer.

1. River Plate, Boca Juniors, Independiente, San Lorenzo de Almagro ____________

2. Bayer Leverkusen, FC Bayern Munich, Dynamo Berlin, VFB Stuttgart ____________

3. Mohan Bagan, Mohammedan Sporting, Salgaokar, Vasco SC ____________

4. Athletic Bilbao, Barcelona, Real Madrid, Sevilla ____________

5. Girondins de Bordeaux, Montpellier Hérault SC, AJ Auxerre, Olympique Lyonnais ____________

MY SCORE

Answers

1. Argentina | 2. Germany | 3. India | 4. Spain | 5. France

ISBN 978-81-8477-610-2

Whether you are an avid sports fan who has to catch every game on TV or a person only remotely concerned with sports, this sports quiz should be pretty easy for you. In the first section, you need to indicate whether the following statements are T = TRUE or F = FALSE. Give yourself a point for each correct answer.

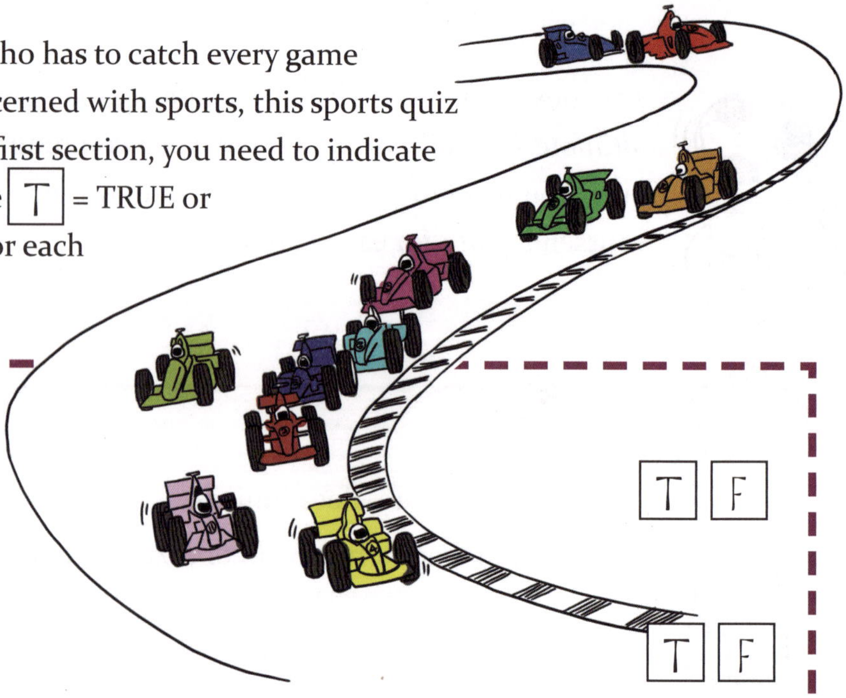

1. The cricketer Martin Crowe plays for Australia. T F
2. Michael and Ralf Schumacher are brothers. T F
3. A chequered flag signifies the start of a Formula One race. T F
4. Prakash Padukone won the Badminton World Cup in 1981. T F
5. Aparna Popat won a bronze medal at the 1998 Commonwealth Games. T F
6. The game of badminton was originally called Poona. T F
7. The first ever Ranji Trophy was won by Mumbai in 1935. T F
8. The Sudirman Cup is awarded in hockey. T F
9. Former cricketer Nasser Hussain played for Bangladesh. T F
10. Leander Paes' father, Vece Paes, represented India in football. T F

 ISBN 978-81-8477-610-2

Answers

1. False | 2. True | 3. False | 4. True | 5. False. She won a silver medal. | 6. True | 7. True
8. False. It is awarded in badminton. | 9. False. He played for England. | 10. False. Vece Paes represented India in Field hockey. He was part of the Indian hockey team that won a bronze medal at the 1972 Munich Olympics.

MY SCORE

In this next quiz, you need to play umpire. In each group below, there lurks "an odd one out". Order the person who doesn't belong in the group back to the stands (but, for the sake of politeness, give a good reason for singling that person as the odd one out). Give yourself a point for each correct answer.

1. Lella Lombardi • Serena Williams • Jenson Button
   Lewis Hamilton • Divina Galica ____________________

2. Zinedine Zidane • Nicholas Sarkozy • Thierry Henry
   Patrick Viera • Fabien Barthez ____________________

3. Michelle Kwan • Evan Lysacek • Oksana Baiul • Elvis Stokjo
   Spongebob Squarepants ____________________

4. Lin Dan • Zhang Ning • Lee Chong Wei • Xie Xingfang • Gong Li
   ____

5. Graeme Smith • Hashim Amla • Kevin Pieterson • Mark Boucher • Albie Morkel
   ____

 ISBN 978-81-8477-610-2

MY SCORE

ANSWERS

1. Serena Williams. She is a tennis player while the others are Formula One drivers. | 2. They are all good-looking Frenchmen but Sarkozy is not a football player like the rest. | 3. Spongebob Squarepants! He is a cartoon character while the others are very famous figure skaters. | 4. All of them are Chinese but Gong Li is an actress while the others are top-ranked badminton players. | 5. Kevin Pieterson. He is member of the English cricket team while the others are members of the South African cricket squad. (*Incidentally*, Pieterson, who was born in South Africa, moved to England so that he could have a better shot at a career in international cricket.)

Finally, to the final section of the Super Sports quiz. You don't really need to sprain your brain much for this quiz—the answers are already given. You just need to make the right choice in this multiple choice quiz. Give yourself a point for each correct answer.

1. In the first 20–20 World Cup in 2007, Yuvraj Singh blasted six sixes in an over. Apart from Yuvraj, only one other Indian has achieved this feat in first class cricket. Who is he?
   a. Kapil Dev
   b. Ravi Shastri
   c. Ajay Jadeja

2. Who is the first Indian woman to win an Asian Games gold in the 400 m run?
   a. Kamaljit Sandhu
   b. P.T. Usha
   c. K. Malleshwari
   d. M.L. Valasamma

3. Which Indian spin bowler was known for bowling maiden overs? He is in the record books for bowling twenty-one successive maiden overs in a Test match.
   a. Subash Gupte
   b. Maninder Singh
   c. E.A.S. Prasanna
   d. R.G. Nadkarni

 ISBN 978-81-8477-610-2

4 Who was the first Indian to win an individual medal at the Olympics?

a. Milkha Singh
b. Karnam Malleshwari
c. K.D. Yadav
d. Abhinav Bindra

5 He is one of the greatest Indian bowlers. He has captained the Indian team and once bowled in a Test match despite a broken jaw!

a. Kapil Dev
b. Anil Kumble
c. Ravi Shastri
d. Sachin Tendulkar

6 The Beighton Cup is associated with

a. hockey.
b. badminton.
c. football.
d. cricket.

7 Who was the first Indian to win the World Amateur Billiards title?

a. Manoj Kothari
b. Geet Sethi
c. Michael Ferreira
d. Wilson Jones

8 Who was the first Indian chess player to win the World Chess Championship for the fifth time in 2012?

a. Dibyendu Barua
b. Praveen Thipsey
c. Vishwanathan Anand
d. Nassir Wajih

9 Who was the first Indian to reach the semi-final round at the Wimbledon Tennis Championship?

a. Leander Paes
b. Ramanathan Krishnan
c. Mahesh Bhupati
d. Ramesh Krishnan

10 In which racquet sport is there a metal board called a telltale on court?

a. Badminton
b. Squash
c. Lawn tennis
d. Table tennis

MY SCORE

Answers

1. b | 2. a | 3. d | 4. c | 5. b | 6. a | 7. d | 8. c | 9. b | 10. b

Final Score

☐ 35–25 Super star!

☐ 24–15 Good sport!

☐ 14 AND BELOW Better luck next time!

 ISBN 978-81-8477-610-2

POWERFUL PERSONALITIES

BET YOU DIDN'T KNOW...

Bet you didn't know that Walt Disney was afraid of mice. Or that Thomas Edison, the bright guy who gave us the first light bulb, was afraid of the dark!

Or that James Garfield, the twentieth president of the United States had a talent that not many others can match. Garfield could write Greek with one hand and Latin with the other—at the same time!

Talking of presidents, did you know that three US presidents have received the Nobel Peace Prize—Woodrow Wilson, Theodore Roosevelt and Barack Obama.

 ISBN 978-81-8477-610-2

Let's see how well you know fun facts about powerful people. To start off the Powerful Personalities quiz, here's a simple match-up quiz. You need to match the leaders to the countries they once headed.

1	Ferdinand Marcos	a.	Vietnam
2	Benazir Bhutto	b.	Former Soviet Union
3	Margaret Thatcher	c.	Cuba
4	Deng Xiaoping	d.	Japan
5	Ariel Sharon	e.	France
6	Fidel Castro	f.	The Philippines
7	Jacques Chirac	g.	Pakistan
8	Michael Gorbachev	h.	Israel
9	Emperor Hirohito	i.	China
10	Ho Chi Minh	j.	United Kingdom

MY SCORE

Answers

1. f | 2. g | 3. j | 4. i | 5. h | 6. c | 7. e | 8. b | 9. d | 10. a

 ISBN 978-81-8477-610-2

That must have been a very easy quiz for a trivia buff like you. On to something a little more complex. In this next quiz, you need to identify what each of these famous personalities are famous for. It's a multiple choice quiz, so the answers are already given. You just need to pick the right option. Give yourself a point for each correct answer.

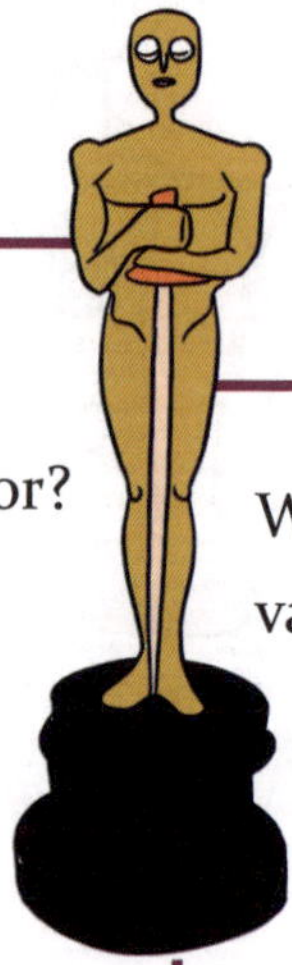

1

Who was the first woman to win the Academy Award for Best Director?

a. Sandra Bullock
b. Oprah Winfrey
c. Kathryn Bigelow
d. Taylor Swift

2

Who invented the first successful vaccine against polio?

a. Louis Pasteur
b. Alexander Flemming
c. Ronald Ross
d. Jonas Salk

3

Who was the first president of Independent India?

a. Dr S Radhakrishnan
b. Jawaharlal Nehru
c. Dr Rajendra Prasad
d. Dr Zakir Husain

4

Who is the present vice-president of India?

a. P.D. Dinakaran
b. L.K. Advani
c. Hamid Ansari
d. Meira Kumar

5

What is the name of the businessman and former Rajya Sabha MP who owns Force India, India's Formula One team, the Indian Premier League team Bangalore Royal Challengers and the I-League team East Bengal FC.

a. Suresh Kalmadi
b. Amitabh Bachchan
c. Lord Swaraj Paul
d. Vijay Mallya

6

Which British king abdicated the throne in 1936 because he was in love with an American divorcée and marrying her would cause big constitutional problems?

a. George V
b. Edward VIII
c. George VI
d. Charles III

 ISBN 978-81-8477-610-2

7 Who is famous for saying "Not everything that can be counted counts and not everything that counts can be counted"?

a. Albert Einstein
b. Oscar Wilde
c. P.G. Wodehouse
d. Alistair MacLean

8 Identify this famous leader: He was an African-American leader. He won the Nobel Prize for Peace at the age of 35. He fought to gain civil rights for African-Americans.

a. Malcolm X
b. Barack Obama
c. Martin Luther King
d. Bill Cosby

9 What is common between U. Thant, Kurt Waldheim, Dag Hammarskjöld and Javier Perez De Cuellar?

a. They are all former Secretary Generals of the United Nations.
b. They are world famous chefs.
c. They are all famous opera singers.
d. They are famous TV anchors.

10 Who painted the ceiling of the Sistine Chapel?

a. Leonardo Dicaprio
b. Leonardo da Vinci
c. Raphael
d. Michaelangelo

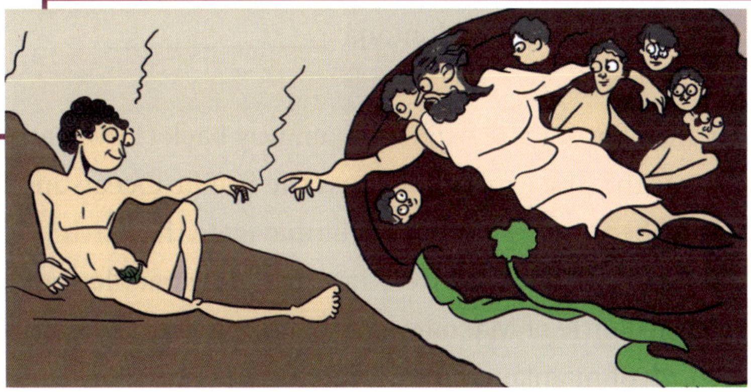

Answers

1. c. In 2010, for her movie *Hurt Locker*. | 2. d | 3. c | 4. c | 5. d | 6. b. Edward VIII was King of the United Kingdom and the British dominions and Emperor of India from 20 January 1936 until his abdication on 11 December 1936. He was given the title of Duke of Windsor after his abdication. | 7. a | 8. c | 9. a | 10. d. Michelangelo di Lodovico Buonarroti Simoni (6 March 1475–18 February 1564), commonly known as Michelangelo, was an Italian Renaissance painter, sculptor, architect, poet and engineer. Michelangelo spent four years painting the Sistine Chapel ceiling. The paint nearly made him go blind and he had to design a dozen new inventions to finish the job. As just one simple example, he invented a new kind of plaster—intonaco—which is still used today. It has a much improved ability to hold the paint properly to the ceiling (useful when painting upside down!) and is also mould resistant.

MY SCORE

 ISBN 978-81-8477-610-2

In this next quiz, you get to play detective. A few clues are given about some very famous people. You need to piece the clues together and guess who these famous people are. Give yourself a point for each correct answer.

1. I am famous for my eponymous (self-titled) talk show. People refer to me as the "Queen of Talk Shows". I run a very successful production company whose name is my name spelt backwards! BTW, I grew up in abject poverty but today I am one of the richest women in the world. ____________________

2. I was the third ruler of the Mughal dynasty and some say I was the greatest emperor of India. I was a great warrior, statesman, patron of art and literature and founder of a new religion—Din-i-Ilahi (but it didn't really catch on!).

   ____

3. I was the first Indian woman to climb the Mount Everest.

   ____

4. I am a famous singer, songwriter and an actress. I am also famous as Hannah Montana. ____________

5. I am a Portuguese explorer from way back (I lived around the sixteenth century). I was the first explorer to cross the Pacific Ocean and an expedition I led became the first to circumnavigate the earth (I couldn't complete the entire voyage because some very inconsiderate people decided to kill me at the Battle of Mactan in the Philippines). The navigable sea route immediately south of mainland South America and north of Tierra del Fuego is named after me. ____________________

6. I am an English actor, model and musician. I was teased in school for wanting to be an actor. I am best known for playing Edward Cullen in the film adaptation of *Twilight*. ____________________

 ISBN 978-81-8477-610-2

7 I founded Facebook, the famous social networking website while a student at Harvard. I now serve as Facebook's CEO. I am one of the world's youngest billionaires.

____

8 I started out as a professor of economics. I founded the Grameen Bank in Bangladesh. ____________________

9 I was originally a Czech citizen but later became a US citizen. I have forty nine Grand Slam titles to my name. I have a massive fan following—tennis star Martina Hingis was named after me. ____________________

10 A lot of people knew me as Gurudev. I am a poet, philosopher, playwright, novelist and visual artist. I was the first (and so far the only) Indian to win the Nobel Prize for Literature. ____________________

MY SCORE

Answers

1. Oprah Winfrey | 2. Akbar | 3. Bachendri Pal | 4. Miley Cyrus | 5. Ferdinand Magellan
6. Robert Pattinson | 7. Mark Zuckerberg | 8. Mohammad Yunus | 9. Martina Navratilova | 10. Rabindranath Tagore

Final Score

- [ ] 30–25 Brilliant!
- [ ] 24–20 Great!
- [ ] 19 and below Better luck next time!

ISBN 978-81-8477-610-2

Who among the following was never a part of the Constituent Assembly (the body that wrote the laws of our country)?

1. Jawaharlal Nehru
2. Mahatma Gandhi
3. Dr B.R. Ambedkar
4. Dr Rajendra Prasad

Answer: Mahatma Gandhi

BET YOU DIDN'T KNOW...

Bet you didn't know that the Constituent Assembly took almost three years (two years, eleven months and seventeen days to be precise) to complete its historic task of drafting the Constitution for Independent India. And FYI, India has the longest written constitution in the world!

 ISBN 978-81-8477-610-2

Let's see how well you know your country. Here are a few really easy questions on India's Constitution. Give yourself a point for each correct answer.

1. India's Parliament is said to be bicameral because
   a. the symbol of the Indian Parliament is a pair of camels.
   b. the Parliament comprises two chambers.
   c. the Parliament holds two sessions a year.

2. The executive head of the Indian Union is the ___________.
   a. prime minister
   b. chief of the army
   c. the president

3. The only state in India to have its own state constitution is ___________.
   a. Chhattisgarh
   b. No state has its own constitution
   c. Jammu and Kashmir

4. The Constitution of India is ___________________.
   a. a written constitution
   b. based on customs and traditions
   c. a combination of written and unwritten elements

5. The Constitution allows for changes to be made in its articles as per the needs of the state. The process by which these changes can be made is called ___________________.
   a. amendments
   b. alterations
   c. corrections

6. The vice-president is elected by the _____________.
   a. president
   b. prime minister
   c. members of Parliament

 ISBN 978-81-8477-610-2

7 Under Article 267, the Constitution provides for money to be placed at the disposal of the president to meet unforeseen expenditure. This is called ________________.

a. splurge as you wish money

b. contingency fund

c. presidential fund

8 The chief minister of a state is appointed by the ________________.

a. the governor of the state

b. prime minister

c. the president

9 The leader of the majority party in Lok Sabha is appointed by the president as the ________.

a. shadow prime minister

b. prime minister

c. vice-president

10 The Directive Principles of State Policy are ________________.

a. a guideline of dos and don'ts for Indian citizens

b. guidelines for the central and the state governments

c. a list of rules for principals

MY SCORE

Answers

1. b | 2. c | 3. c | 4. a | 5. a | 6. c | 7. b | 8. a | 9. b | 10. b

 ISBN 978-81-8477-610-2

If you read the newspapers, especially the business section, this next quiz should be a breeze for you. You need to match these famous Indian business heads to the organisations they head. Give yourself a point for each correct match.

1	Kiran Mazumdar Shaw	a.	The Future Group
2	Azim Premji	b.	Hong Kong and Shanghai Bank (HSBC)
3	Naina Lal Kidwai	c.	Kinetic Engineering
4	Sunil Mittal	d.	Biocon
5	Chanda Kocchar	e.	Wipro
6	Kishore Biyani	f.	Arcellor Mittal
7	Indra Nooyi	g.	ICICI
8	Lakshmi Mittal	h.	Tata Group of Companies
9	Cyrus Mistry	i.	Pepsico
10	Sulajja Firodia Motwani	j.	Bharti

MY SCORE

Answers

1. d | 2. e | 3. b | 4. j | 5. g | 6. a | 7. i | 8. f | 9. h | 10. c

 ISBN 978-81-8477-610-2

Here's the final Incredible India quiz. Crack this crossword to discover how well you know your country. Give yourself a point for each clue you can solve correctly.

ACROSS

3. The famous Gol Gumbaz, Mysore Palace and ruins of Hampi are located in this state (its capital is Bengaluru).
4. This state has the second highest literacy rate in the country; it shares its boundary with Bangladesh and Myanmar (its capital is Aizawl).
5. A state famous for lal maas, blue pottery, sand dunes and wildlife.
7. The famous Bhimbekta rock paintings, Sanchi Stupa and Khajuraho group of monuments are located in this state (its capital is Bhopal).
8. A state famous for kakori kebabs and the Taj Mahal.
9. A state famous for its Chhat festival, Madhubani paintings and the Mahabodhi Temple.
10. Capital of the union territory of Andaman and Nicobar Islands.

DOWN

1. A northern state famous for rogan josh, gustaba and haak (it's also the only state with its own Constitution).
2. The smallest union territory in India comprising twelve atolls, three reefs and many submerged banks (its capital is Kavaratti).
6. A state famous for Kathakali, houseboats and snake boat races (its capital is Thiruvananthapuram).

 ISBN 978-81-8477-610-2

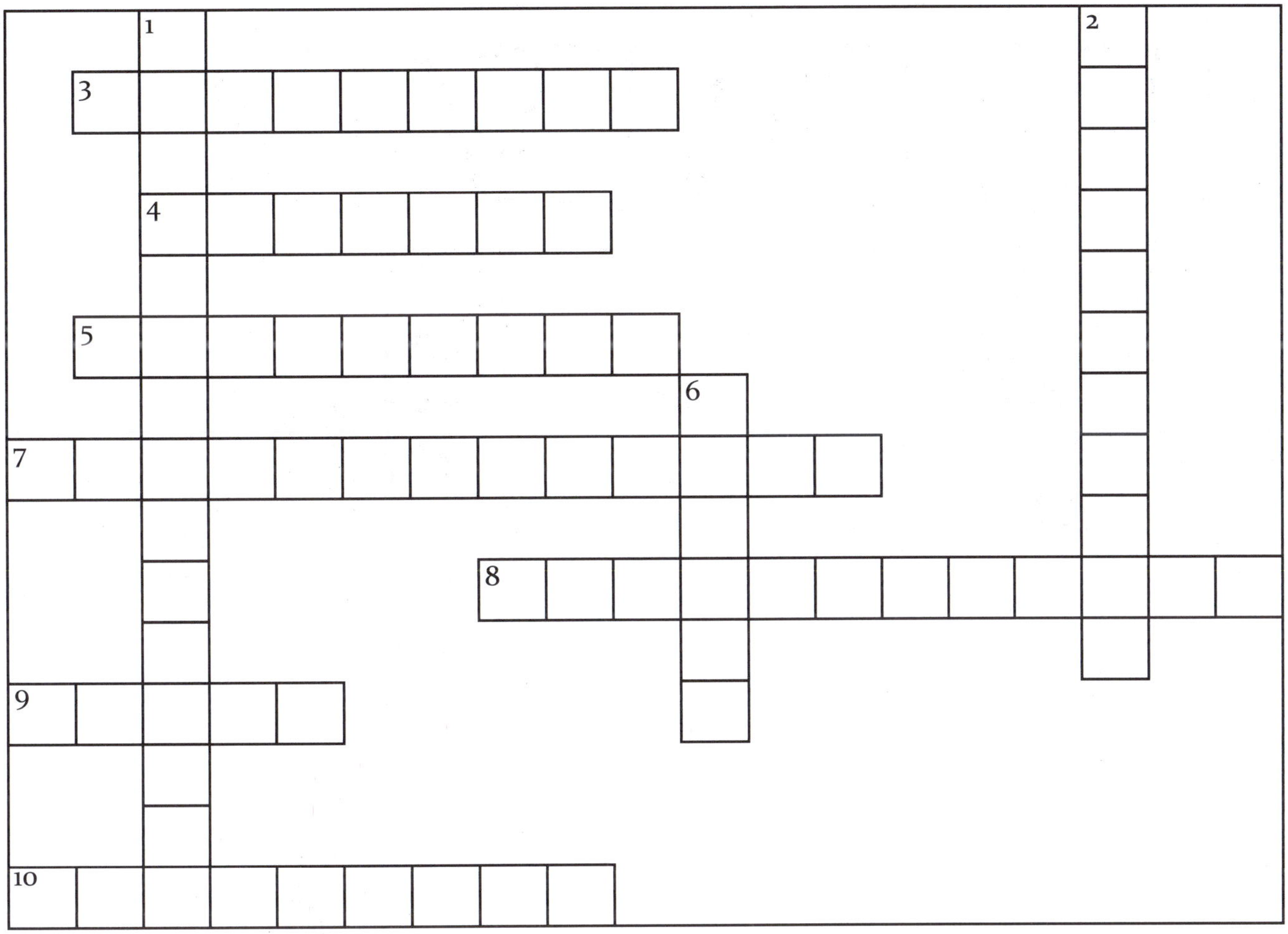

MY SCORE

Answers

ACROSS - 3. Karnataka | 4. Mizoram | 5. Rajasthan | 7. Madhya Pradesh
8. Uttar Pradesh | 9. Bihar | 10. Port Blair

DOWN - 1. Jammu and Kashmir | 2. Lakshadweep | 6. Kerala

Final Score

- ☐ 30–25 Incredible Indian!
- ☐ 24–15 Okay!
- ☐ 14 AND BELOW Try harder next time!

 ISBN 978-81-8477-610-2

EFFERVESCENT ENGLISH

Have you ever wondered why **caregiver** and **caretaker** mean the same thing? Or how you are supposed to get off a **non-stop** flight? Or if a race is **neck and neck**, would that mean it's a **necktie**? English can be a crazy and confusing language at times.

 ISBN 978-81-8477-610-2

Here's a quiz on some words that kids (and a lot of adults!) often get mixed up. Choose the correct option in the sentences below and give yourself a point for each correct answer. Give yourself a bonus point if you get all the answers correct.

1. I have three pairs of trousers and I can't find (any / some) of them.
2. I didn't get home (by / until) midnight last night.
3. Rishab and Preeti are waiting for a bus. (They're / Their) waiting at the bus stop.

4. If I could (borrow / lend) your bicycle, I could go home quickly and fetch the book you want.
5. The government has been trying to (control / check) spending.
6. The noise outside the auditorium (effected / affected) my performance.
7. It is all right to (accept / except) gifts from your friends.
8. The colours green and blue (complement / compliment) each other perfectly.
9. I (bought / brought) myself some books and a big box of chocolates with the money my aunt sent me for my birthday.
10. Her mother works (at / in) the bank.

MY SCORE + BONUS POINT =

Answers

1. any | 2. until | 3. They're | 4. borrow | 5. control | 6. affected
7. accept | 8. complement | 9. bought | 10. at

 ISBN 978-81-8477-610-2

BET YOU DIDN'T KNOW...

Bet you didn't know about the myth about the word "quiz". It is said that it was invented in 1782 by James Daly, a theatre manager in Dublin. He once had a bet with a friend that he could introduce a new word into the English language in a day. He then had the word quiz chalked on all the walls of the city. Everyone who saw it started talking about it. Daly won the bet and we got a pretty useful word!

 ISBN 978-81-8477-610-2

Here's an interesting English language quiz for you. Match up the idioms to their meanings. Give yourself a point for each correct answer.

	Idiom		Meaning
1	To let the cat out of the bag	a.	to settle an old quarrel
2	To bury the hatchet	b.	to be honored or rewarded for an act
3	To build castles in the air	c.	to have the advantage of enjoying it both ways
4	To have a feather in one's cap	d.	to have the same fate as someone else
5	To upset the apple cart	e.	to have wild fun specially during a night outing
6	To look up to someone	f.	to disrupt plans or ruin something
7	To put one's cards on the table	g.	to be open and reveal everything
8	To paint the town red	h.	to admire and respect someone
9	To sail in the same boat	i.	to let a secret out
10	To have one's cake and eat it too	j.	to plan something that can never come true

MY SCORE

Answers

1. i | 2. a | 3. j | 4. b | 5. f | 6. h | 7. g | 8. e | 9. d | 10. c

 ISBN 978-81-8477-610-2

In the next quiz, your English language skills and your powers of reasoning will be put to the test. You need to complete the word analogies given below and also indicate whether you have chosen to use an antonym or a synonym. To make things a little easy for you, the word choices are given in the box below. Best of luck! Give yourself a point for each correct answer. Give yourself a bonus point if you can answer all the questions correctly.

adept ● remarkable ● broken ● speedy ● miniscule ● hurdle ● powerful ● daring

1. Pretty is to attractive as strong is to ____________. SYNONYM / ANTONYM
2. Big is to huge as tiny is to ____________. SYNONYM / ANTONYM
3. Finished is to incomplete as intact is to ____________. SYNONYM / ANTONYM
4. Fall is to tumble as jump is to ____________. SYNONYM / ANTONYM
5. Brave is to meek as fearful is to ____________. SYNONYM / ANTONYM
6. Nice is to pleasant as fast is to ____________. SYNONYM / ANTONYM
7. Happy is to joyful as skillful is to ____________. SYNONYM / ANTONYM
8. Negative is to affirmative as ordinary is to ____________. SYNONYM / ANTONYM

MY SCORE [ ] + BONUS POINT [ ] = [ ]

Answers

1. powerful (synonym) | 2. miniscule (synonym) | 3. broken (antonym) | 4. hurdle (synonym)
5. daring (antonym) | 6. speedy (synonym) | 7. adept (synonym) | 8. remarkable (antonym)

 ISBN 978-81-8477-610-2

Here's the final section of the Effervescent English quiz. You need to figure out the mystery words given below. The starting letter of each mystery word is provided along with the number of letters that make up the word and its three synonyms. So, go on, solve this quiz. You have a time limit of five minutes. Give yourself a point for each correct answer.

1	a ___ ___ ___ ___ ___	soak, imbibe, sop up
2	a ___ ___ ___ ___ ___	foolish, idiotic, preposterous
3	D ___ ___ ___ ___ ___	delay, procrastinate, dilly-dally
4	N ___ ___ ___	(Hint: It's a slang word.) dweeb, fool, simpleton
5	W ___ ___ ___ ___ ___ ___	fighter, combatant, soldier
6	C ___ ___ ___ ___ ___ ___	catch, bag, net
7	P ___ ___ ___	duo, couple, brace
8	B ___ ___ ___	publication, volume, tome
9	M ___ ___ ___ ___ ___	defiance, revolt, uprising
10	T ___ ___ ___ ___ ___ ___	educator, pundit, tutor

MY SCORE

Answers

1. absorb | 2. absurd | 3. dawdle | 4. nerd | 5. warrior | 6. capture | 7. pair | 8. book | 9. mutiny | 10. teacher

Final Score

☐ 40–35 Topnotch performance!

☐ 34–25 Commendable performance!

☐ 24–15 Competent performance!

☐ 14 and below Abominable performance!

 ISBN 978-81-8477-610-2

BRILLIANT BRAINTEASERS

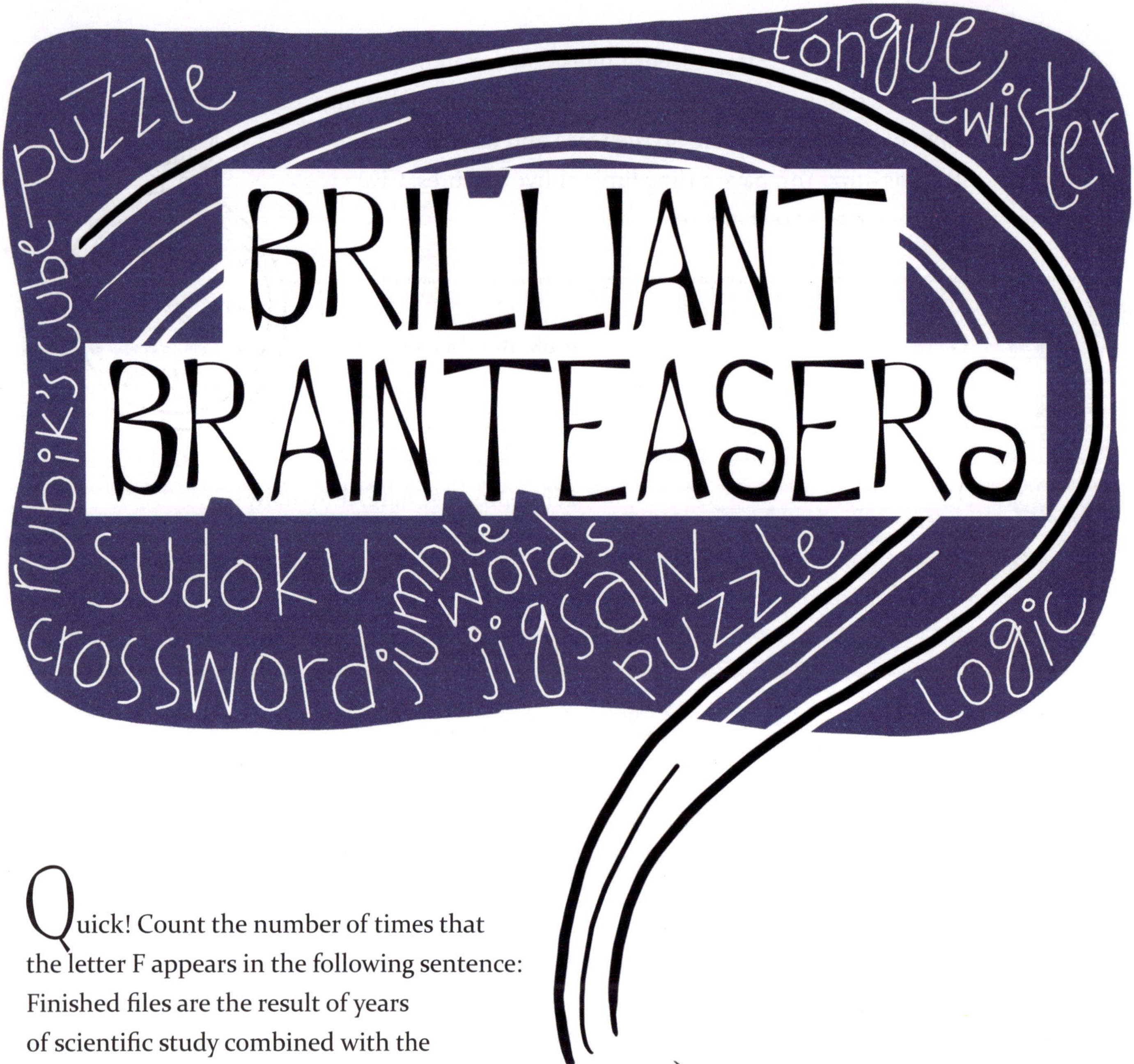

Quick! Count the number of times that the letter F appears in the following sentence:
Finished files are the result of years of scientific study combined with the experience of years.
How many did you find? Three? Wrong, there are six!
Almost everyone guesses three.
Why? It seems that the brain cannot correctly process the word "OF". The letter F usually makes the "f" sound, like in "fox".
However, in the word "of", it makes a "v" sound.
Somehow, your brain overlooks the word "of" as it scans for the sound of "f".

 ISBN 978-81-8477-610-2

Perform the calculation below as fast as you can using only mental arithmetic (without pen and paper or a calculator!). Give yourself five points if you get the answer correct.

TAKE 1,000 AND ADD 40.

ADD 1,000.

ADD 30 AND THEN ADD 1,000.

ADD 20.

ADD 1,000 AND THEN ADD 10.

WHAT IS THE RESULT OF THIS CALCULATION?

ANSWER

Most people get 5,000 as result, if they perform the calculation as fast as they can. But the answer is 4,100. Because of the hurry, the tens and the hundreds get mixed up in the last step (4,090 plus 10).

MY SCORE

 ISBN 978-81-8477-610-2

Below are ten words which have been split in half. The first column has all the starts and the second column has all the ends. Can you pair the letters and remake all ten words? Give yourself ten points if you get all ten words. Give yourself five bonus points if you can find all ten words in less than fifteen minutes.

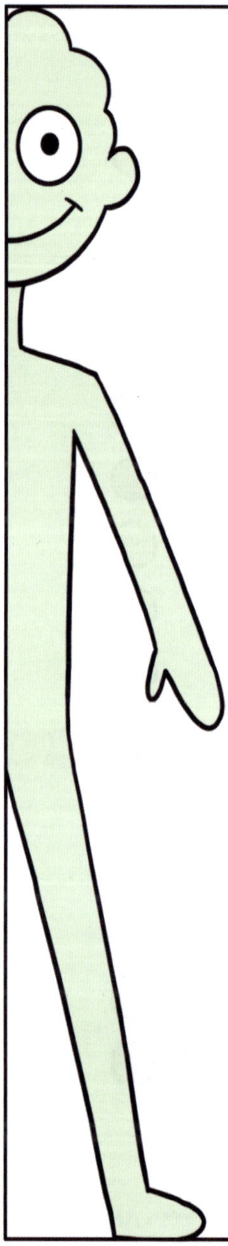

BO	AF
BR	RE
FO	NE
GO	AF
HO	KE
JO	EW
LE	ON
LO	AM
LI	LD
SO	PE

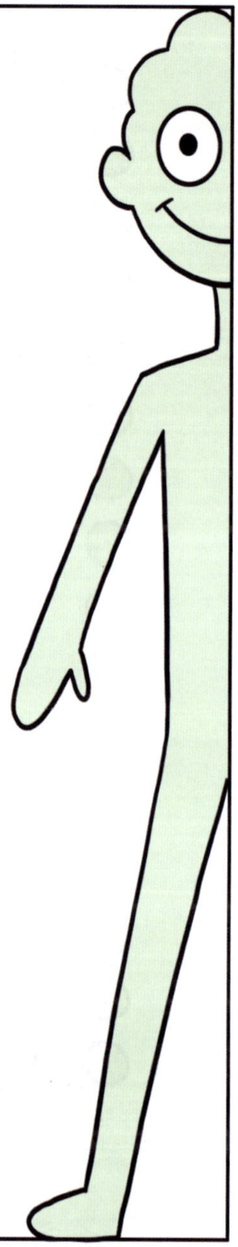

MY SCORE + BONUS POINTS =

ANSWERS

bold/bone/bore, brew, foam, gone/gold/gore, hope, joke, leaf, loaf, lion, sore/sold

 ISBN 978-81-8477-610-2

Can you make five squares using twelve toothpicks?

Answer: Make a square with each side made of two toothpicks. Now, divide up this giant square into four smaller squares using the four remaining toothpicks (each toothpick should be placed from the midpoint of each side to the centre of the big square).

Here are a few more brainteasers. Give yourself a point for each question you solve correctly.

1. Veena is taller than Meena. Beena is taller than Veena. Sheena is not shorter than Veena. Who is the shortest of the four? __________

2. Prateek can clean his parents' car in forty minutes and Javed can clean the same car in sixty minutes. How long will it take for them to clean the car together? __________

3. Shweta walks 3 km straight, turns right and walks 4 km straight. She then turns right and travels 6 km straight again. How far is she from the starting point? __________

4. In thirty years, Ashok will be four times older than he is now. How old is Ashok? __________

 ISBN 978-81-8477-610-2

5 Write the missing number in the sequence:
7, 15, 32, ___, 138, 281 ____________

6 Kevin's grandfather gave him twice as much pocket money that his grandmother gave him. He spent half of the money he got from his grandparents on a new book for himself. The book cost him ₹150. How much money did his grandmother give him? ____________

7 A rectangle has a length of 6.5 cm and a width of 3.5 cm. What is its area? ____________

8 (56.27 x 100) + (65.35 x 10) = ? ____________

9 If today Leena is two times older than she was seven years ago, what is her present age? ____________

10 I got a book at a 40 per cent discount. If I paid ₹372 for it, what was the original cost of the book? ____________

MY SCORE

ANSWERS

1. Meena | 2. Twenty-four minutes | 3. 5 km (you need to apply Pythagoras Theorem) | 4. Ten-years old
5. 67 | 6. ₹100 | 7. 22.75 cm^2 | 8. 6280.5 | 9. Fourteen years | 10. ₹620

 ISBN 978-81-8477-610-2

Here's the final section of the Brainteaser Quiz. This is an analogy quiz. You need to figure out the analogy in the given statements and complete it. The answer is given in brackets—you just need to make the logical and correct choice. Give yourself a point for each correct answer.

1. Celsius is to temperature as watt is to (electrical power / James Watt)

2. Square is to cube as circle is to (sphere / rectangle)

3. Victoria Memorial is to Kolkata as India Gate is to (India / New Delhi)

4. Star is to rats as reward is to (failure / drawer)

5. Canberra is to Australia as Oslo is to (Norway / Finland)

MY SCORE

Answers

1. electrical power | 2. sphere | 3. New Delhi | 4. drawer | 5. Norway

Final Score

☐ 35–25 Brilliant!

☐ 24–20 Bright kid!

☐ 19 AND BELOW Bland performance!

 ISBN 978-81-8477-610-2

MARVELLOUS MOVIES, BOOKS AND MUSIC

william shakespeare william wordsworth lewis caroll roald dahl agatha christie tolstoy jane austen munshi premchand tagore

BET YOU DIDN'T KNOW...

Bet you didn't know that British poet Lord Tennyson spent his childhood lying in a churchyard among the graves! *How creepy is that?* Did you know that William Wordsworth (the famous poet who wrote "Daffodils") often wrote about flowers and yet had no sense of smell!

 ISBN 978-81-8477-610-2

Over the years, some movies have taken their storylines as well as their titles from works of famous novelists. Match these famous novels, which have been made into very famous movies, to their authors. Give yourself a point for each correct match.

1 *Devdas*	a. Jane Austen
2 *Vanity Fair*	b. Roald Dahl
3 *The Namesake*	c. Frank L Baum
4 *The Wizard of Oz*	d. Bankim Chandra Chatterjee
5 *Godaan*	e. Rabindranath Tagore
6 *Pride and Prejudice*	f. William Makepeace Thackeray
7 *Twilight*	g. Munshi Premchand
8 *Kabuliwala*	h. Stephanie Meyer
9 *Anandmath*	i. Sarat Chandra Chattopadhyay
10 *Matilda*	j. Jhumpa Lahiri

MY SCORE

ANSWERS

1. i | 2. f | 3. j | 4. c | 5. g | 6. a | 7. h | 8. e | 9. d | 10. b

 ISBN 978-81-8477-610-2

Time to play party planner! Imagine a very swish party is being planned and the virtual who's who of the entertainment world is on the guest list. The host wants to make sure that only people who have things in common sit together at dinner tables spread across a huge garden. A really dumb person made up the lists and has made some huge mistakes. Your job is to make sure that each list of dinner guests is accurate and does not have any odd one out. If you happen to spot one, delete that name from the list right away. Give yourself a point for each odd one out that you spot on the list of dinner guests.

GUEST CHECKLIST

1. Beethovan • Mozart • Brahms • Picasso • Schubert
2. Bhimsen Joshi • Vijay Mallya • Dr Balamuralikrishna
Kishori Amonkar • Bombay Jayashri
3. Jhumpa Lahiri • A.O. Hume • Vikram Seth • Salman Rushdie • Anita Desai
4. Elton John • George Michael • Mick Jagger • James Cameron • Julio Iglesias
5. Dilton • Reggie • Betty • Veronica • Hobbes
6. Sandra Bullock • Angela Merkel • Reese Witherspoon • Angelina Jolie • Hilary Swank
7. Douglas Adams • Dav Pilkey • Pete Sampras • Eoin Colfer • R.L. Stine
8. Taylor Swift • Cheryl Tweedy • Nelson Mandela • Nelly Furtado • Colbie Callait
9. James Cameron • Rajkumar Hirani • Yusuf Pathan
Woody Allen • Shyam Benegal
10. Sonu Nigam • Sunidhi Chauhan • J.K. Rowling
Gayatri Iyer • Kunal Ganjawala

 ISBN 978-81-8477-610-2

Answers

1. This would be a ghostly table to be at (ALL of them are dead!) but the odd one out would be Picasso. He was a world famous painter while the others were famous composers. | 2. Vijay Mallya. He is a renowned industrialist but the others are famous exponents of Indian classical music. | 3. A.O. Hume. He was an Englishman who played a major role in establishing the Indian National Congress. The others are all famous authors. | 4. James Cameron is a famous director (his latest was *Avatar*) while the others are famous singers. | 5. Hobbes. Hobbes is a tiger and Calvin's constant companion (from the comic strip *Calvin and Hobbes*). The others are characters from *Archie*. 6. Angela Merkel. Angel Merkel is the present German Chancellor while the others are Oscar award-winning actresses. | 7. Pete Sampras. He is a famous tennis player but isn't (as yet) an author like the other dinner guests on this list. | 8. Sorry but you'll have to delete Nelson Mandela from the list. He is a much loved world leader but he might feel out of place with the other dinner guests who are all famous singers. | 9. Yusuf Pathan. He is a cricketer while the others are movie directors. | 10. You'll have to cross out J.K. Rowling from this list. She is an author while the others on the list are playback singers.

MY SCORE

 ISBN 978-81-8477-610-2

GUESS THE MOVIE

1. A famous film based on a Broadway Musical. It is the story of seven children who need a governess. The film also has a very popular song "Do-Re-Mi". ____________

2. A little baby gets kidnapped by a trio of bumbling criminals. The three goons have a hard time keeping hold of the baby, who definitely seems to be smarter than the three goons put together. ________________

3. An eight year old child gets left behind at home while his family jets off to France for Christmas vacation. Not only does the little boy manage to take care of himself, he manages to foil two robbers who decide to break into his home. ____________________

4. This film was released way back in 1966. It is a real life story about a couple who raised a lion cub "Elsa" and then released her into the wilderness of Kenya. ____________

5. The story of an out-of-luck songwriter and three adorable chipmunks he adopts. ____________________

MY SCORE

ANSWERS

1. *The Sound of Music* | 2. *Baby's Day Out* | 3. *Home Alone* | 4. *Born Free* | 5. *Alvin and the Chipmunks*

FINAL SCORE

☐ 25–20 Brilliant!

☐ 19–15 Great!

☐ 14 AND BELOW Better luck next time!

 ISBN 978-81-8477-610-2